STOCKING STUMPERS

FOOTBALL
2012

By S. Claus

RED-LETTER PRESS, INC.
Saddle River, New Jersey

STOCKING STUMPERS - FOOTBALL

Copyright ©2012 Red-Letter Press, Inc.
ISBN-10: 1-60387-103-9
ISBN-13: 978-1-60387-103-7

Red-Letter Press, Inc.
P.O. Box 393, Saddle River, NJ 07458
www.Red-LetterPress.com
info@Red-LetterPress.com

ACKNOWLEDGMENTS
SANTA'S SUBORDINATE CLAUSES

Editor:
Jeff Kreismer

Contributor:
Jack Kreismer

Cover & Page Design:
Cliff Behum

Special Mention:
Sparky Anderson Kreismer

INTRODUCTION

Whether you're having a few quiet
moments to yourself or enjoying a
reunion with friends and family, Stocking
Stumpers is the perfect holiday companion.
Gather 'round the Christmas tree or simply
kick back in your easy chair while
trying out the holiday humdingers,
tailor-made tests and trivia tidbits.

Once you've had a sampling, I think you'll
agree, Stocking Stumpers is proof of the
Christmas pudding that good things do
come in small packages. Ho ho ho!

Merry Christmas!!

S. Claus

The Mantle Meter

'Tis right around Christmas
and all through the book,

There are all sorts of stumpers
everywhere that you look.

There are quizzes and seasonal tests
to take you to task,

But what are those "stocking"
questions you ask?

Well, the stockings are hung
by the chimney with care.

The more that are filled,
the tougher the bear.

And so it is that
the Mantle Meter keeps score,

Rating the stumpers,
one stocking or more.

STOCKING STUMPERS

FOOTBALL
2012

THIS YEAR IN FOOTBALL

1. In May of 2012, what former Rutgers player was ceremoniously signed by the Tampa Bay Buccaneers?

2. With the Giants hosting the Cowboys, why did the 2012 regular season begin on a Wednesday rather than its usual Thursday slot?

3. In 2006, he was inducted into the Seahawks Ring of Honor. In '07, he was named the best athlete ever to wear #96 by SI.com. In 2012, he was inducted into the Pro Football Hall of Fame.

4. Which top pick in the 2012 NFL Draft has a father who quarterbacked in the NFL: Andrew Luck or Robert Griffin III?

5. ESPN moved to a two-man booth for the 2012 *Monday Night Football* season after dismissing what analyst?

What NFL team used to play at Veterans Stadium?

ANSWERS

1.

Eric LeGrand, who was paralyzed during a 2010 game against Army

2.

To avoid conflict with the last day of the Democratic National Convention

3.

Cortez Kennedy

4.

Andrew Luck, whose dad, Oliver, played in Houston in the 1980s

5.

Ron Jaworski (Mike Tirico and Jon Gruden remain.)

Philadelphia Eagles

ON THE MARK

1. He and Joe Flacco are the only two rookie starting quarerbacks in NFL history to win two playoff games.

2. After the 1982 strike-shortened season, he became the only kicker in NFL history to be named the league's MVP.

3. He was the Giants starting tight end in the team's first two Super Bowl wins.

4. As a Redskin in 2006, he set an NFL record for the most consecutive completions in a game, 22.

5. He won the 2009 Heisman Trophy in the closest vote in the award's history.

What three quarterbacks threw for over 5,000 yards during the 2011 NFL season?

ANSWERS

1.
Mark Sanchez

2.
Mark Moseley

3.
Mark Bavaro

4.
Mark Brunell

5.
Mark Ingram

Drew Brees, Tom Brady and Matthew Stafford

A TALL ORDER

1. "Too Tall" Jones was a 6'9"
defensive end for Dallas. What
is his given first name?

2. This 6'8" quarterback was drafted 16th
overall in 1991 by the Seahawks. His
brother was an MLB star. Name the pair.

3. What 6'8" receiver was named
to four Pro Bowls during his time
with the Eagles in the 1970s?

4. What 6'9" offensive tackle was
named to the NFL 2000s
All-Decade Team as a Raven?

5. This 6'7" defensive end played both
football and basketball at UNC before he
was drafted in 2002 by Carolina. Name him.

What football legend was the NFL's first President?

ANSWERS

1.

Ed

2.

Dan McGwire, and
brother Mark McGwire

3.

Harold Carmichael

4.

Jonathan Ogden

5.

Julius Peppers

Jim Thorpe

ALPHABET SOUP

1. If football's Hall of Famers were listed alphabetically, who would come first?

2. His real name is O.A. Phillips, but you can call him Bum. Do you know, though, what his initials stand for?

3. His last name is 14 letters long, and with 112 catches, he was tops in the NFL in receptions in 2007. Who is he?

4. Of all NFL quarterbacks whose last names begin with the letter Z, who has thrown the most touchdown passes?

5. During the 2008 season, why did all NFL players have the initials "GU" on their jerseys?

How many Super Bowls has Dan Marino won?

ANSWERS

1.

Herb Adderley

2.

Oail Andrew

3.

T.J. Houshmandzadeh

4.

Jim Zorn

5.

In honor of Gene Upshaw, the head of the NFL Players' Association, who died that summer

THE COMBINE

1. The NFL Scouting Combine is a week-long showcase for college prospects that occurs in what Indianapolis venue?

2. What running back's 40-yard dash time of 4.24 seconds at the 2008 NFL Combine helped elevate him to a first round draft pick?

3. What 2012 Cowboys first round pick scored a reported 4 out of 50 on the Wonderlic Test?

4. In arguably the best combine performance to date, what tight end's dazzling display of speed and strength vaulted him into the draft's top ten in 2006?

5. This troubled running back posted two poor 40-times before walking out on the rest of the drills in 2005, earning him the nickname "Slow-Mo."

❄ SEASONAL STUMPER ❄

This recording artist, with the same name as an *NFL Today* broadcaster, had a 1988 Christmas album called *Santa's Got a Brand New Bag.*

ANSWERS

1.

Lucas Oil Stadium

2.

Chris Johnson

3.

Morris Claiborne

4.

Vernon Davis

5.

Maurice Clarett

Seasonal Stumper Answer:

James Brown

ANIMAL PLANET

1.

How many NFL teams have bird nicknames?

2.

What member of the famed Steel Curtain defense was nicknamed "Mad Dog"?

3.

This team's offensive line, a huge key to their three Super Bowls from 1982-91, was known as "The Hogs".

4.

What two former NFL quarterbacks were both nicknamed "The Snake"?

5.

"Papa Bear" was the owner of Chicago's NFL franchise for over 60 years. What's his real name?

Who coached Andrew Luck at Stanford before moving on to the NFL in 2011?

ANSWERS

1.

5 - Cardinals, Eagles,
Falcons, Ravens, Seahawks

2.

Dwight White

3.

Washington Redskins

4.

Ken Stabler and Jake Plummer

5.

George Halas

Jim Harbaugh, with the 49ers

THE INJURY REPORT

1. What 2009 football film includes footage from Lawrence Taylor's 1985 sack of Joe Theismann, which caused Theismann's career-ending leg injury?

2. What Patriots star tore his ACL and MCL in the final game of the 2009 NFL season, forcing him to miss the playoffs?

3. What future Hall of Famer suffered a career-ending injury in Philadelphia in 1999 and was cheered by Eagles fans as he went off on a stretcher?

4. In 1985, what defensive back had part of his injured finger amputated so he would not miss a playoff game?

5. In 2008, coming off another shoulder surgery, who was named the NFL's Comeback Player of the Year for the second time?

What NFL team was formerly known as the Decatur Staleys?

ANSWERS

1.

The Blind Side

2.

Wes Welker

3.

Michael Irvin

4.

Ronnie Lott

5.

Chad Pennington

Chicago Bears

TOUCHING DOWN

1.

Who is the NFL's all-time
leader in career touchdowns scored?

2. In 2004, what quarterback became the
first ever to throw for over 30 TDs and
less than 10 interceptions in one season?

3. True or False: LaDainian Tomlinson
had at least 10 rushing touchowns
in each of his 11 NFL seasons.

4. What two men with the same last
name have each scored over 10
touchdowns off interception returns?

5. Who's the only player in NFL history to
throw 50 passing TDs in a single season?

In 2008, what AFC team won their division after
having just one victory the previous season?

Answers

1.

Jerry Rice, 208

2.

Donovan McNabb

3.

False - He did, however, in each of
his first nine years in San Diego.

4.

Rod Woodson and Charles Woodson

5.

Tom Brady, in 2007

Miami Dolphins

THE MAN

Which players were the heroes of these famous moments in NFL history?

1. The Catch - Joe Montana hit this man in the end zone to win the 1981 NFC Championship.

2. The Drive - Cleveland fans were heartbroken when this quarterback led his team 98 yards down the field enroute to the AFC title.

3. The Miracle at the Meadowlands - Giants QB Joe Pisarcik fumbled a handoff while running out the clock and this Eagle ran in the game-winning score.

4. The Hail Mary - The term became widespread after this Dallas QB hit Drew Pearson with a last-second prayer in a 1975 playoff game to beat the Vikings.

5. The Catch III - Over a decade after Terrell Owens made "The Catch II", this 49er hauled in an Alex Smith pass to beat the Saints in the 2011 Playoffs.

❄ SEASONAL STUMPER ❄

Christmas Card Lane and Friars Road are both street names in San Diego, the latter (9449 Friars Road, to be exact) where the Chargers home is located. What is the stadium's name?

ANSWERS

1.
Dwight Clark

2.
John Elway

3.
Herman Edwards

4.
Roger Staubach

5.
Vernon Davis

Seasonal Stumper Answer:
Qualcomm Stadium

PIGSKIN POTPOURRI

1.
Where will Super Bowl XLVII be held on February 3, 2013?

2.
The current NFL commissioner is Roger Goodell. Can you name the previous two?

3.
How many football teams play in the Big 10 football conference?

4.
Was the minimum salary for an NFL rookie in 2012:
a. $190,000 b. $290,000
c. $390,000 d. $790,000

5.
After Joe Paterno was stripped of 111 of his career wins at Penn State, who became the winningest coach in Division 1 football history?

Who is the only player to have his number retired by the Buffalo Bills?

ANSWERS

1.

At the Mercedes-Benz
Superdome in New Orleans

2.

Paul Tagliabue and Pete Rozelle

3.

12

4.

C

5.

Grambling's Eddie Robinson

Jim Kelly, #12

FUNNY BUSINESS

1.
What football funny, a blunderful one at that, do Roy Riegels and Jim Marshall have in common?

2.
What former NFL head coach was featured in a humorous beer commercial ranting, "Playoffs!? You kiddin' me? Playoffs!? Don't talk about playoffs!"

3.
What former NFL coach was famous for leaving tickets for Elvis Presley at will-call on game day?

4.
What three NFL quarterbacks have hosted *Saturday Night Live* in the 21st century?

5.
"Fair Hooker, that's a great name, isn't it? But I haven't met one yet." What "dandy" announcer said that when referring to the Cleveland Browns wide receiver in the first *MNF* game ever?

What former Buffalo Bills kicker is often associated with "wide right"?

ANSWERS

1. Both recovered fumbles and ran the wrong way. In the 1929 Rose Bowl, Riegels ran 69 yards before being tackled by his teammate on the one. In 1964, the Vikings Marshall raced 66 yards into his own end zone for a safety.

2.

    Jim Mora

3.

    Jerry Glanville (Elvis was a no-show for obvious reasons.)

4.

    Tom Brady, Peyton Manning and Eli Manning

5.

    Don Meredith, in the Browns 31-21 win over the NY Jets

Scott Norwood, from his missed kick that would have won Super Bowl XXV against the Giants

INITIALLY SPEAKING

The answers to the following clues each have the same first and last initial.

1. In his 2011 Hall of Fame induction speech, he said, "I'm the second-best player in my own family." Who is he, and who was he referring to?

2. He is most famous for scoring the winning touchdown in "The Greatest Game Ever Played", the 1958 title game against the Giants.

3. He was the first NFL player to record a 150-yard receiving game in three different decades.

4. What career Steeler started every game at center for Pittsburgh from 1989-98?

5. He and the answer to #3 are the only two players to catch over 120 passes in at least two separate seasons.

What NFL star's college basketball jersey is retired by Kent State?

ANSWERS

1.

Shannon Sharpe (brother Sterling)

2.

Alan Ameche

3.

Cris Carter

4.

Dermontti Dawson

5.

Wes Welker

Antonio Gates

UNIFORMITY

Each current NFL QB below wears the same jersey
number as a Hall of Famer on the right. Match them up.

1. Aaron Rodgers   a. John Elway

2. Cam Newton   b. Terry Bradshaw

3. Drew Brees   c. Fran Tarkenton

4. Michael Vick   d. Sonny Jurgensen

5. Eli Manning   e. Warren Moon

What former defensive end is
credited with coining the term "sack"?

ANSWERS

1.

B - #12

2.

E - #1

3.

D - #9

4.

A - #7

5.

C - #10

Deacon Jones

Colorful Characters

1. With a stellar debut season in 2011, what rookie was quickly dubbed the "Red Rifle"?

2. What defensive star was the first player in NFL history to have his number officially retired by multiple teams?

3. He was the first wide receiver ever to win the Heisman Trophy, doing so in 1987.

4. Who were the Purple People Eaters?

5. Following the 2011 season, he became the first rookie receiver to make the Pro Bowl in nearly a decade.

❄ Seasonal stumper ❄

What former New Jersey Generals USFL owner appeared as himself in the Christmas sequel *Home Alone 2*?

ANSWERS

1.

Andy Dalton

2.

Reggie White, with the
Eagles and Packers

3.

Tim Brown

4.

The standout defensive line of the
Minnesota Vikings from
the late '60s to '70s

5.

A.J. Green

Seasonal Stumper Answer:

Donald Trump

COLLEGE CORNUCOPIA

1. In 2011, this school had a rule named after them stating that all playing fields must remain green, and not be in another color like the blue turf at Bronco Stadium.

2. What Sun Belt school was attended by pash rushing experts DeMarcus Ware and Osi Umenyiora?

3. What school lost the BCS National Championship Game in back-to-back years to Florida (2006) and LSU (2007)?

4. Alabama produced two Top 10 picks in the 2012 NFL Draft. Who were they?

5. With alumn including Jonathan Vilma and Vince Wilfork, what school set the record for the most first rounders taken in a single draft, with six in 2004?

In the last 40 years, only one defensive player has won the Heisman Trophy. Who is it?

ANSWERS

1.

Boise State

2.

Troy University

3.

Ohio State

4.

Trent Richardson and Mark Barron

5.

University of Miami

Charles Woodson

LOOK WHO'S 50!

All of these athletes turned the big 5-0 in 2012.

1. He was the first athlete to be named an All-Star in two major American sports - football and baseball.

2. After nearly a decade-long absense from the league, this quarterback was the NFL's Comeback Player of the Year in 1998.

3. In 2010, he was selected #1 all-time in the NFL Films production *The Top 100: NFL's Greatest Players*.

4. He was a five-time Pro Bowl tight end from 1991-95 who won three Super Bowl rings in that time period.

5. He won the 1982 Heisman and is the only player in NCAA history to finish in the top three in the voting every season he played college football.

With Peyton Manning out for the year, who quarterbacked the Colts to their only two wins of 2011?

ANSWERS

1.
   Bo Jackson

2.
   Doug Flutie

3.
   Jerry Rice

4.
   Jay Novacek

5.
   Herschel Walker

Dan Orlovsky

TU"FF" GUYS

The last names of the following players all have "ff" somewhere in them.

1. This Raiders Hall of Famer had ten consecutive seasons of 40 or more receptions from 1967-76.

2. He's college football's only two-time Heisman winner.

3. He holds the record for the most touchdown passes in a single game by a modern-era rookie, with five in 2009.

4. He and Jason Smith are the only two Baylor players to be picked in the NFL Draft's top ten in the last 25 years.

5. After Keith Jackson's one year with *Monday Night Football*, who became the second play-by-play man in 1971?

Who was the first head coach to make four Super Bowl appearances?

ANSWERS

1.

Fred Biletnikoff

2.

Archie Griffin

3.

Matthew Stafford

4.

Robert Griffin III

5.

Frank Gifford

Don Shula

BACKING UP

1. Before he became Houston's quarterback, Matt Schaub put in his time as a three-year backup with what team?

2. While he's one of the greatest athletes ever, Bo Jackson wasn't technically a starter for the Raiders. What legendary running back was he behind?

3. What backup QB led the Bills to victory with an improbable 32-point comeback over the Oilers in the 1992 playoffs?

4. An unknown Kurt Warner took the NFL by storm in 1999 after what Rams starter went down in the preseason?

5. What Packers receiver, with just four catches all season, helped Green Bay win Super Bowl I with seven catches and two scores?

❄ SEASONAL STUMPER ❄

This president was only able to celebrate two Christmas holidays in the White House, yet had a Philadelphia stadium named after him, one that hosted the Army-Navy game more than any other venue. Name him.

ANSWERS

1.

Atlanta Falcons

2.

Marcus Allen

3.

Frank Reich

4.

Trent Green

5.

Max McGee

Seasonal Stumper Answer:

John F. Kennedy (JFK Stadium hosted the
football classic from 1936-79 with the
exception of three years during World War II.)

THE TONYS

1. In 1989, *Sports Illustrated* called him "the best offensive line prospect ever", but he is now considered one of the biggest busts in NFL history.

2. In 2002, this QB became the first player in Eastern Illinois history to win the Walter Payton Award, given annually to the top NCAA Division I-AA player.

3. This future All-Pro was the first draft pick in the history of the Jacksonville Jaguars, going #2 in 1995.

4. An All-Pro tight end, he was also a college basketball player at Cal, where he played in the Sweet Sixteen in the 1990s.

5. This former Dolphins head coach became the offensive coordinator of the Jets in 2012.

Who is the NFL's all-time sack leader?

ANSWERS

1.

Tony Mandarich

2.

Tony Romo

3.

Tony Boselli

4.

Tony Gonzalez

5.

Tony Sparano

Bruce Smith, with 200

THE OLYMPICS

1. What gold medal sprinter at the 1964 Olympics played three seasons as a Giants defensive back and once scored on a 101-yard interception return?

2. While he never played in the league, what legendary track and field athlete was drafted in the 12th round of the 1984 NFL Draft by the Cowboys as a wide receiver?

3. What Pro Football Hall of Famer is the only person to have received a Super Bowl ring and an Olympic gold medal?

4. What two-time All-Pro running back competed in the 1992 Winter Olympics in the two-man bobsled?

5. Before he became a Raider, what appropriately named sprinter was a gold medalist from the 1992 U.S. 4 x 100 meter relay team?

Lou Holtz's only head coaching job in the NFL was with what team?

ANSWERS

1.

Henry Carr

2.

Carl Lewis

3.

Bob Hayes

4.

Herschel Walker

5.

James Jett

New York Jets

PLAYING BY THE RULES:
COLLEGE VS. PRO

1.
Are the hash marks on an NFL
field narrower or wider than
those on the college gridiron?

2.
When a first down is made,
the clock is stopped. Is this in
a college or pro game?

3.
Does college football have a
two-minute warning?

4.
In the NFL, the ball is spotted on the
two-yard line for an extra point
conversion. Where is it placed in college?

5.
True or False: The goalposts are
the same width in both
college and professional football.

What was the nickname of the defense of
the undefeated 1972 Miami Dolphins?

ANSWERS

The No-Name Defense

POP QUIZ

1. David, a quarterback, was drafted by Green Bay in 1977. His son, Charlie, was Seattle's QB when they won the division at 7-9 in 2010. What is their last name?

2. Dick Nolan and his son, Mike, have each served as the head coach of what NFL team?

3. Hall of Famer Howie Long's son, Chris, was drafted #2 overall by what team in 2008?

4. What Super Bowl-winning coach has a father who played for the Lions and then served as an assistant coach at Navy for 33 years?

5. The father of Green Bay's Clay Matthews (also named Clay) was a multiple All-Pro linebacker for what team in the 1980s?

❄ SEASONAL STUMPER ❄

It was the day after Christmas in 1960 when the Eagles defeated the Green Bay Packers for the NFL championship, 17-13. The game featured a Philadelphia offensive center/linebacker, the NFL's last 60-minute man. Who was he?

ANSWERS

1.

Whitehurst

2.

San Francisco 49ers

3.

St. Louis Rams

4.

Bill Belichick
(His father is Steve Belichick.)

5.

Cleveland Browns

Seasonal Stumper Answer:
Chuck Bednarik

SINGLE DIGITS

The answers to the following clues are all from 1-9.

1.
How many rounds does the
NFL Draft currently have?

2.
The score of a forfeited
NFL game is ___ to 0.

3.
How many active NFL franchises have
yet to appear in a Super Bowl?

4.
In their first two NFL seasons,
the Tampa Bay Buccaneers won
how many total games?

5.
Curtis Martin edged out Shaun
Alexander for the 2004
rushing title by how many yards?

What stadium, which closed its doors to
NFL play in 1996, has been referred to as
"The Eighth Wonder of the World"?

ANSWERS

1.

7

2.

2

3.

4 - Cleveland Browns, Detroit Lions,
Jacksonville Jaguars and Houston Texans

4.

2

5.

1

Houston Astrodome

MASCOT MANIA

Match up these mascots with the NFL teams they represent.

1. Rowdy   a. Texans

2. Captain Fear   b. Vikings

3. Toro   c. Buccaneers

4. Ragnar   d. Bengals

5. Who Dey   e. Cowboys

In his expansion team's first season, what quarterback
was sacked a league record 76 times in 2002?

ANSWERS

1.

E

2.

C

3.

A

4.

B

5.

D

David Carr

CENTURY TEST

Determine whether each event occured in the 20th or 21st century.

1.

The New England Patriots win
their first Super Bowl title.

2.

Future Hall of Famer Barry
Sanders played in his final NFL game.

3. The Eagles converted on "4th and 26",
going on to beat Green Bay and reach
their third straight NFC title game.

4.

The Houston Texans expansion
franchise played its first NFL game.

5.

Brett Favre won his third
consecutive MVP award.

What NFL player is the grandson of
Uganda's first Prime Minister?

ANSWERS

1.

21st - Super Bowl XXXVI in 2002

2.

20th - 1998

3.

21st - 2004

4.

21st - 2002

5.

20th - 1997

Mathias Kiwanuka, grandson
of Benedicto Kiwanuka

HOME, SWEET HOME

1.
The street address where they
play their home games is
One Paul Brown Stadium. They are...?

2.
One of the league's biggest stadiums sits
on 1600 FedEx Way. Who plays there?

3.
Their state of the art stadium is
located at One Legends Way in
Arlington. Name the team.

4.
They play at 347 Don Shula Drive.
For extra credit, of what
significance is the "347"?

5.
Here's a gift from Santa:
What team calls 1265
Lombardi Avenue home?

❄ SEASONAL STUMPER ❄

It was Christmas Eve in 1974 when the
Packers named the MVP of Super Bowls I
and II their head coach. Who was he?

ANSWERS

1.

Cincinnati Bengals

2.

Washington Redskins

3.

Dallas Cowboys

4.

Miami Dolphins - Shula had 347 career wins as a head coach.

5.

Green Bay Packers

Seasonal Stumper Answer:

Bart Starr

MONEY MATTERS

All of the following answers have monetary-related last names.

1. He took over Pat Summerall's job as the lead play-by-play man for the NFL on Fox in 2002.

2. A member of the NFL's 1980's All-Decade Team, he recorded 14 tackles in the Giants Super Bowl XXI victory.

3. On November 14, 1993, they became the firsts twins in NFL history to catch a touchdown pass on the same day.

4. After a 2002 breakout season in Buffalo in which he surpassed 1,200 receiving yards, he moved on to Atlanta, where he was "less" than stellar.

5. As a rookie starter at QB for the Rams in 1996, he set a new NFL record for fumbles, with 21.

What NFL team has the #12 retired in honor of its fans, the "twelfth man"?

ANSWERS

1.

Joe Buck

2.

Carl Banks

3.

Keith and Kerry Cash

4.

Peerless Price

5.

Tony Banks

Seattle Seahawks

SPORTSMEN OF THE YEAR

We've provided the years and the Super Bowl credentials. It's your job to uncover these *Sports Illustrated* honorees.

1. 2005: He's the only quarterback to start and win three Super Bowls before the age of 28.

2. 1990: He started at quarterback in four Super Bowls and won them all.

3. 1979: Super Bowl XIII marked the first time in his career that he surpassed 300 yards passing.

4. 1993: He coached five different quarterbacks to Super Bowl appearances.

5. 2010: In his first Super Bowl, he tied the game's record with 32 pass completions.

What college did wide receivers Wes Welker and Danny Amendola attend?

ANSWERS

1.
Tom Brady

2.
Joe Montana

3.
Terry Bradshaw

4.
Don Shula

5.
Drew Brees

Texas Tech

THINK PRESIDENT!

1.

He holds the record for the
longest play in Super Bowl history.

2.

On his decision not to vote in 1996,
this former Raiders Pro Bowl tackle
said, "I was going to write myself
in, but I was afraid I'd get shot."

3.

He's the only player in NFL history
to run three kickoffs back for
touchdowns in two separate seasons.

4.

He was the winner of the 2005 Heisman
Trophy ("was" being the key word).

5.

He led the NFL in receiving in 1968. The
following year, he became the first Steeler
with back-to-back 1,000-yard seasons.

Who is Megatron?

ANSWERS

1.

James Harrison, with a
100-yard interception return
for a TD in Super Bowl XLIII

2.

Lincoln Kennedy

3.

Leon Washington

4.

Reggie Bush

5.

Roy Jefferson

Calvin Johnson

WHO SAID IT?

1. In 2008, following a 13-13 stalemate with the Bengals, this quarterback revealed, "I've never been a part of a tie. I never even knew that was in the rule book."

2. According to this 13-time Pro Bowl selection, "I feel like I'm the best, but you're not going to get me to say that."

3. On his quarterback, Jim McMahon, he once said, "We have a strange and wonderful relationship. He's strange and I'm wonderful."

4. Amidst the Patriots "Spygate" controversy in 2007, this former Charger joked that New England lived by the saying, "If you ain't cheatin', you ain't tryin'."

5. This coach praised one of his best players by saying, "Earl (Campbell) may not be in a class by himself, but whatever class he's in, it doesn't take long to call the roll."

The Cleveland Browns retired the uniform number of Ernie Davis after he died of leukemia without having played a single NFL game. What was his number?

ANSWERS

1.

Donovan McNabb

2.

Jerry Rice

3.

Mike Ditka

4.

LaDainian Tomlinson

5.

Bum Phillips

ODD MAN OUT

Which of the following did *not*...

1.

Win a rushing title:
Curtis Martin, Priest Holmes,
Ricky Williams or Fred Taylor?

2.

Rush for five touchdowns in a single game:
Clinton Portis, Walter Payton
Jim Brown or Ricky Watters?

3.

Win a Super Bowl ring:
Roger Staubach, Ken Stabler,
Fran Tarkenton or Phil Simms?

4.

Play for the Los Angeles Rams:
Joe Namath, Franco Harris,
Jerome Bettis or Ron Jaworski?

5.

Beat the Eagles in the NFC
Championship Game:
Cardinals, Panthers,
Falcons or Buccaneers?

❄ SEASONAL STUMPER ❄

This Christmas baby was born in 1945 and
would become the first left-handed
quarterback to win the Super Bowl. Name him.

ANSWERS

1.

Fred Taylor

2.

Walter Payton

3.

Fran Tarkenton

4.

Franco Harris

5.

Falcons

Seasonal Stumper Answer:

Ken Stabler

1, 2, 3

Designate the following in the order they rank.

1.

Most Super Bowl titles:
Cowboys, Steelers, Patriots

2.

Career passing yards:
Peyton Manning, Dan
Marino, Brett Favre

3.

Highest draft pick:
Tom Brady, Tony Romo, Aaron Rodgers

4.

Number of NFL teams coached:
Bill Belichick, Bill Parcells, Bill Walsh

5.

Most 1,000-yard rushing seasons:
Jerome Bettis, Emmitt
Smith, Earl Campbell

The Atlanta Falcons traded five draft picks
in order to move up and grab what wide
receiver in the 2011 NFL Draft?

ANSWERS

1.

Steelers (6), Cowboys (5) and Patriots (3)

2.

Favre, Marino, Manning
(They are the Top 3 all-time.)

3.

Rodgers (#24 overall), Brady
(#199), Romo (undrafted)

4.

Parcells (4), Belichick (2), Walsh (1)

5.

Smith (11), Bettis (8), Campbell (5)

Julio Jones

FOREIGN FLAVOR

1. While he has a Nigerian first name, which means "from today things will be good", this Giant was born in London. Who is he?

2. The NFL's all-time leading scorer was born in Denmark. Name him.

3. In 2007, where did the Giants and Dolphins play the first ever regular season NFL game outside of North America?

4. What Norwegian and member of the College Football Hall of Fame coached Notre Dame in the early 20th century?

5. NFL _____ was a type of developmental league where pro teams placed players until it ceased operation in 2007.

With what team did quarterback Derek Anderson make the Pro Bowl in 2007?

ANSWERS

1.

Osi (Ositadimma) Umenyiora

2.

Morten Andersen

3.

London's Wembley Stadium
(The Giants won, 13-10.)

4.

Knute Rockne

5.

Europe

Cleveland Browns

LAST NAME'S THE SAME

1.

Pat and Kevin, who formed
a "wall" together

2.

Charles "Peanut" and NFL hero
Pat, both defensive backs

3.

Jim and Leonard, former Pro
Bowl defensive linemen

4.

Tim and Lomas, each of whom has
played in over 250 career NFL games

5.

Hall of Famers Jim and Leroy

What Pro Bowl quarterback of the Vikings was
also drafted by the New York Yankees in 1995?

ANSWERS

1.

Williams (They were the "Williams Wall" on Minnesota's defensive line.)

2.

Tillman

3.

Marshall

4.

Brown

5.

Kelly

Daunte Culpepper

THE LONGEST YARD

1. In 2011, before they met in the Super Bowl, two receivers had 99-yard touchdown receptions. Name them.

2. The longest touchdown pass in Super Bowl history occurred in Super Bowl XXXVIII, when what two Carolina Panthers hooked up for an 85-yard score?

3. He's credited with the longest play in NFL history, a 109-yard TD return off a missed field goal in 2007.

4. The longest run from scrimmage in Super Bowl history, a 75-yard score in Super Bowl XL, belongs to what player?

5. The longest touchdown pass of Terry Bradshaw's NFL career went for 90 yards. What fellow quarterback was on the receiving end?

❄ SEASONAL STUMPER ❄

It was a merry Christmas for Franco Harris and company after he made the December 23, 1972, "Immaculate Reception" – a fourth down desperation pass from Terry Bradshaw to give Pittsburgh a playoff win over what team?

ANSWERS

1.

Wes Welker and Victor Cruz

2.

Jake Delhomme and
Muhsin Muhammad

3.

Antonio Cromartie

4.

Willie Parker

5.

Mark Malone
(The catch would be the first,
and last, of Malone's career.)

Seasonal Stumper Answer:

The Oakland Raiders

KEEPING SCORE

We give you the score, date and place. You provide the event.

1.

21-17: December 31, 1967
at Lambeau Field.

2.

51-45: January 10, 2010
at University of Phoenix Stadium.

3.

16-7: January 12, 1969
at the Orange Bowl.

4.

72-41: November 27, 1966
at D.C. Stadium.

5.

62-7: January 15, 2000
at Alltel Stadium.

Who is the only placekicker in the
Pro Football Hall of Fame?

ANSWERS

1. In what became known as the Ice Bowl, Bart Starr led his Packers over the Cowboys for the NFL Championship.

2. The highest-scoring postseason game in NFL history occurred as the Cardinals beat the Packers in overtime.

3. Joe Namath's guarantee proved true as the Jets upset the Colts in Super Bowl III.

4. The Redskins defeated the Giants in the highest-scoring game in NFL history.

5. In what would be Dan Marino's last NFL game, the Dolphins were destroyed by the Jaguars in the AFC Divisional Round of the playoffs.

Jan Stenerud

Hamming It Up

1. What 1970s Steelers Hall of Fame linebacker was nicknamed Dobre Shunka?

2. His NFL claim to fame comes as the man who replaced Emmitt Smith in Dallas when Smith left for Arizona in 2003.

3. Fred Williamson was an All-Star defensive back in the AFL who went by what nickname throughout his career?

4. He was the only Giants running back in the 1990s to be named to the Pro Bowl.

5. He's known as Big Snack and has been a mainstay on the Steeelers defensive line for over a decade. Name him.

What team holds the record for the most consecutive wins in Division I college football?

ANSWERS

1.

Jack Ham (Dobre Shunka translates to "Good Ham")

2.

Troy Hambrick

3.

The Hammer

4.

Rodney Hampton

5.

Casey Hampton

Oklahoma, 47 in a row from 1953-57

CATCHING ON

1. In 1961, what Denver Bronco became the first professional football player to catch 100 passes in a single season?

2. Set in 2007, what receiver holds the NFL record for the most catches in his first two seasons?

3. In 2011, what two players broke the single-season record for the most receiving yards by a tight end?

4. Who are the only two running backs in NFL history to gain 1,000 yards rushing and 1,000 yards receiving in the same season?

5. In 2005, who became the first undrafted free agent ever to have 10,000 career receiving yards?

In 2009, who broke Terrell Owens' NFL record by catching 21 passes in a single game?

ANSWERS

1.

Lionel Taylor

2.

Marques Colston

3.

Jimmy Graham and Rob Gronkowski

4.

Roger Craig (1985) and
Marshall Faulk (1999)

5.

Rod Smith

Brandon Marshall

WHAT'S WHAT?

1.
What is a punt that goes
out of bounds just before
reaching the goal line called?

2.
What is unique about the
helmets of the Pittsburgh Steelers?

3.
What was the Music City Miracle?

4.
What is Thomas Morstead's
"Super" NFL claim to fame?

5.
By what nickname is the last pick in
the NFL Draft every year known?

❄ SEASONAL STUMPER ❄

The Chicago Bears and Green Bay Packers
played on Christmas night last year, when a
quarterback threw the first 5-touchdown game of
his career. Was it Aaron Rodgers or Jay Cutler?

ANSWERS

1.

A coffin corner kick

2.

They're the only NFL team to have their logo on just one side of the helmet.

3.

In the 1999 Playoffs, the Titans beat the Bills on a last-second kickoff return score by Kevin Dyson off a lateral from Frank Wycheck.

4.

Morstead started the second half of Super Bowl XLIV vs. the Colts with an onside kick that gave New Orleans possession, and ultimately their first lead of the game.

5.

Mr. Irrelevant

Seasonal Stumper Answer:

Aaron Rodgers

MDs

1. He was an "MD" until his days at UCLA, when he made an addition to his name to honor his late grandfather.

2. In 1988, he became the first tight end inducted into the Pro Football Hall of Fame.

3. He and Mark Clayton entered the Dolphins Ring of Honor together in 2003.

4. In 2010, after failing to kick the ball out of bounds, this Giants punter allowed DeSean Jackson and the Eagles to create a second "Miracle at the Meadowlands."

5. This Oklahoma running back's career was the subject of an ESPN 30 for 30 film, *The Best That Never Was.*

Jim Kelly and Steve Young began their professional football careers in what league?

ANSWERS

1.

Maurice Drew (now Jones-Drew)

2.

Mike Ditka

3.

Mark Duper

4.

Matt Dodge

5.

Marcus Dupree

USFL

QB Scramble

Unscramble the combined first and last names of these quarterbacks who all played into their 40s.

1.

NETSREDVITVANYE

2.

TRAFBETEVR

3.

ROENAWMRON

4.

MLOERLARLRA

5.

GOFTUILUDE

What punter holds the NFL record for consecutive games played, with 352?

ANSWERS

1.

Vinny Testaverde

2.

Brett Favre

3.

Warren Moon

4.

Earl Morrall

5.

Doug Flutie

Jeff Feagles

PLAYING BY THE RULES

1. The quarterback catches his own pass. May he throw another forward pass?

2. In a PAT situation, does the defensive team have an opportunity to score points?

3. A defensive player intercepts a pass in his own end zone. He attempts to run it out, but is tackled in his own end zone. Is it ruled a safety?

4. A defensive lineman tips the quarterback's pass. A cornerback then pushes a receiver to the ground, intercepts the ball and returns it for a score. Does the TD count?

5. A field goal attempt is blocked and bounces back to the kicker. May the kicker then drop-kick it through the uprights?

LeRoy Butler was credited with starting what touchdown celebration in 1993?

ANSWERS

1.

No

2.

No - If the defensive team gains possession, the play is ruled dead.

3.

No - It's ruled a touchback for the intercepting player's team.

4.

Yes - As long as the push occurs after the pass is tipped, there is no penalty.

5.

Yes

Lambeau Leap

Super Bowl Shuffle

Match up the following Super Bowl scores with
the teams that played in the games.

1. SB I: Packers over Chiefs   a. 55-10

2. SB VI: Cowboys over Dolphins   b. 17-14

3. SB XXIV: 49ers over Broncos   c. 35-10

4. SB XLII: Giants over Patriots   d. 31-17

5. SB XLIV: Saints over Colts   e. 24-3

Coach Tom Coughlin played in the same backfield
with Floyd Little and Larry Csonka at what college?

ANSWERS

1.

C

2.

E

3.

A

4.

B

5.

D

Syracuse University

THE END

With which teams did these players finish their pro football careers?

1.

Junior Seau

2.

LaDainian Tomlinson

3.

Brett Favre

4.

Steve McNair

5.

Shaun Alexander

❄ SEASONAL STUMPER ❄

Which is the greater number- the amount of "Golden Rings" in the *Twelve Days of Christmas* or wide receivers who have won the Super Bowl MVP?

ANSWERS

1.

New England Patriots

2.

New York Jets

3.

Minnesota Vikings

4.

Baltimore Ravens

5.

Washington Redskins

Seasonal Stumper Answer:

There were six MVP wideouts and five golden rings.